The GRAND Taskmaster

by Barbara A. Donovan
illustrated by Maurie Manning

Harcourt
SCHOOL PUBLISHERS

Printed in China

ISBN 10: 0-15-350557-5
ISBN 13: 978-0-15-350557-7

Ordering Options
ISBN 10: 0-15-350335-1 (Grade 5 Below-Level Collection)
ISBN 13: 978-0-15-350335-1 (Grade 5 Below-Level Collection)
ISBN 10: 0-15-357558-1 (package of 5)
ISBN 13: 978-0-15-357558-7 (package of 5)

5 6 7 8 9 10   468   12 11 10 09

Characters

Liz, host

Joshua, player

Ashley, player

Michael, player

Narrator

Narrator: As the show begins, Liz walks out onto the stage. A throng of people who make up the audience claps loudly for her. Liz waves and then bows to them.

Liz: Thank you very much! You are one boisterous audience! Welcome to *The Grand Taskmaster*. Players on our show have to perform certain tasks. Some of the jobs are practical. Others are just for fun. The one who wins the most tasks becomes our Grand Taskmaster. We have three great players with us today: Ashley, Michael, and Joshua. Welcome!

Ashley, Michael, and Joshua: Thank you!

Liz: Can you each give us some insight into your life and tell us about yourself? Ashley, you go first.

Ashley: Hello, Liz! I'm a chess master. I've been playing chess since I was five.

Liz: That's a great feat! Maybe all the deductions you make while playing chess will help you win this game. Michael, what do you like to do?

Michael: I love to cook. When I grow up, I plan to work in the food industry and maybe own my own restaurant. My chocolate cake has won prestigious awards.

Liz: Good for you! Our third player is Joshua. I hear that you went on a wild trip. Tell us about it.

Joshua: For our last family vacation, I proposed that we go camping. My parents thought it was a great idea. While we were camping, I took pictures of many wild animals. Here's a picture of some elk. Here is one of a mother bear and her cubs.

Liz: My instinct would be to run if I saw a bear. You took a picture. Weren't you scared?

Joshua: No, I wasn't. That's because we were quite far away from the bear. I used a zoom lens on my camera. It seems like the bear was close, but it wasn't. Actually, what really scared me was the invasion of mosquitoes!

Liz: I can understand how mosquitoes could be very unpleasant! Now it's time to play *The Grand Taskmaster*. I will give you a task. The one who completes the task fastest wins the round. The first player to win five rounds wins the game. Are you ready?

Narrator: Joshua, Ashley, and Michael nod their heads. A curtain in the center of the stage opens. The audience members laugh when they see three portable sinks and a stack of dirty dishes beside each sink.

Liz: Your first task is to wash a stack of dishes. Each of you may take a place at a sink. When I say *go*, you may begin washing. The player who gets the most dishes clean in one minute wins this round. *Ready? Set? Go!*

7

Narrator: Joshua, Ashley, and Michael dip their arms in the suds and start washing the dishes. Ashley scours the dishes quickly while the whole audience cheers her on. By the time the buzzer sounds to end the round, Joshua has washed a measly four dishes. Michael has washed nine dishes. Ashley has washed fifteen dishes.

Liz: Ashley is the clear master of this task! Ashley, tell us how you did all those dishes so fast.

Ashley: My job at home is to wash the dishes each night. I have learned how to wash dishes quickly so that I can see my favorite TV show.

Liz: Let's see if you will be fast enough at the other tasks to be today's Grand Taskmaster. Open the curtain so that we can see the next task.

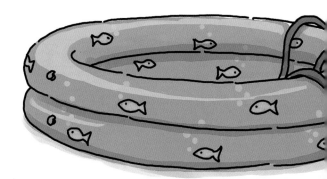

Narrator: The curtain on the left side of the stage opens. On the stage are three tanks of water. Hand pumps protrude from the tops of the tanks. A hose runs from each tank into a child's swimming pool.

Liz: This task is also a race. The first one to pump all of the water from his or her tank into the swimming pool wins. Take your places!
Ready? Set? Go!

Narrator: Ashley and Michael have a hard time getting their water to circulate through the pumps and into their hoses. They are baffled about how to make the pump work properly. Meanwhile, Joshua works the pumping device smoothly. The fickle audience begins cheering for Joshua. In no time at all, Joshua's water tank is dry. A grin creases Joshua's face when he realizes he has won this task.

Liz: Joshua is the master of this task! Tell us how you did this, Joshua.

Joshua: It was easy. This hand pump is a lot like the one I use to fill up my little sister's swimming pool.

Liz: Well, all your experience helping with your sister's pool really paid off. The score is one round for Ashley and one round for Joshua.

Narrator: Play continues for several more rounds. Now Ashley and Michael each have four points. Joshua has three points. The curtain at the center stage opens for the final task. A laundry basket sits on each of three tables.

Liz: Take your places at the table. Now look in the basket in front of you. Each basket is filled with socks. You must match the appropriate socks and roll them in pairs. The player who correctly matches the greatest number of socks  wins this task. If it's Ashley or Michael, that player will win the game. If Joshua wins this task, then it's a tie, and we'll have to continue this game again on tomorrow's show. *Ready? Set? Go!*

Narrator: Ashley dumps her basket onto the table. She spreads the socks out so that she can see them all. Ashley quickly sorts through the socks and tosses each rolled pair of socks into the empty basket. Before long, Joshua and Michael dump their baskets out, too, and they start catching up to Ashley. Soon Michael and Ashley only have a few pairs of socks left to match. Suddenly, Ashley notices that one pair of socks doesn't match. She has to go back and find the matching socks. While she is looking, Michael rolls his final pair of socks. He tosses them into his basket. Michael starts jumping up and down with excitement.

Liz: You did it, Michael! You are today's Grand Taskmaster! How did you roll those socks so quickly?

Michael: In addition to being a good cook, I'm also an artist. I have a good eye for color. It was easy for me to match the socks in my basket. I also have to admit that Ashley's idea of dumping out the socks really helped me. Thanks, Ashley.

Ashley: You're welcome, I think.

Joshua: Congratulations, Michael. You played a great game.

Liz: Yes, congratulations. We have a special prize package picked out just for you, Michael.

Narrator: A curtain on the right side of the stage opens up.

Liz: You have won a complete set of baking pans and an electric mixer!

Narrator: Michael is very excited. He grins and shakes everyone's hand.

Liz: That's all the time we have for today. Please join us tomorrow in our search for the next Grand Taskmaster!

Think Critically

1. What is this book about?

2. Why was Ashley's decision to dump out all the socks for sorting better than Joshua and Michael's way of sorting the socks in the basket?

3. Which of the three tasks that the players performed on *The Grand Taskmaster* would have been easiest for you? Why?

4. Why is the part of the Narrator important in this and other Readers' Theaters?

5. Michael admitted that Ashley's idea for dumping out the socks helped him. What does this tell you about Michael's character?

 **Language Arts**

Plan a Taskmaster Game Make a list of five tasks that you would include in a Taskmaster Game. Write the rules for each of these tasks.

School-Home Connection Summarize the story for a family member. Then talk about some tasks that you could help with around your home.

Word Count: 1,158